★ Contents ★

Stories for ★ ★

4
Year Olds

First published 2018 by Brown Watson

The Old Mill, 76 Fleckney Road

Kibworth Beauchamp

Leicestershire LE8 0HG

ISBN: 978-0-7097-2536-7

Brown Watson

ENGLAND

 # The Pet Unicorn

Jake is fast asleep and dreaming happy dreams.
He is woken by a noise. 'Lucy! Lucy! Wake up!'
he whispers to his sister.

The children climb out of bed and follow the noise. It leads them outside into their garden. 'Oh wow!' they gasp. 'A unicorn!'

The unicorn has hurt its leg and needs their help. They ask Daddy to call the vet the very next day.

The vet tells them to take good care of their new pet. She keeps their secret safe. Everyone else thinks they have got an ordinary pony!

Harry's Magic Hammer

Harry has a very special toy. If he holds his hammer and wishes really hard, it takes him on amazing adventures.

Yesterday, Harry learned about dinosaurs at school. When he got home, he used his hammer to carry him back to prehistoric times.

Harry's daddy told him about his adventures in the desert. Harry makes a wish, and his hammer transports him there in a flash.

'Where shall we go tomorrow?' Harry asks his puppy. He gazes up at the Moon in the night sky. 'Great idea!' smiles Harry.

The Tidy Ladybird

Lacey Ladybird has invited her friends to tea.
She spends all morning tidying her house.
It is sparkling clean!

In the afternoon, she cleans the windows and tidies the garden. She brushes and scrubs and sings a little song.

Later, she bakes cakes and makes sandwiches. When she has finished, she cleans the kitchen one more time.

Lacey has one more job to do. She polishes her shell until it gleams. Beautiful! Now she can't wait for her friends to arrive!

Play Time

Little Blue, the dolphin, loves to have fun beneath the ocean waves. 'Will you play with me?' he asks the fish. But they just swim away.

Little Blue swims to the surface. He spots a bird flying close to the water. 'Do you want to play?' The bird squawks and flies off.

Little Blue dives deep to the ocean floor. 'Will you play a game?' he asks the starfish. But the starfish is stuck to the seabed.

Poor Little Blue! He swims along sadly until he hears clicks and whistles. It is his family, who want him to join in all their games.

# Lost and Found

Poor Teddy is afraid. He was left in the park by Alfie, and is lying all alone in the grass. How will he get home?

Alfie misses Teddy. He searches everywhere, but Teddy has gone. An unusual friend offers to help.

'Follow me!' says Squirrel. 'We'll find him.' He rushes towards a tree with a hidden doorway in the trunk.

They climb up and up. 'You can see for miles!' says Squirrel. Sure enough, from up here, Alfie can see exactly where Teddy is lying.

Weather Warning

It is a warm, sunny day and Maisie Mouse is very busy. She puts out the rubbish and goes to the shops.

While she is shopping, she feels a drop of rain on her twitchy nose. 'Oh! I must hurry home! They said there will be a storm today.'

Maisie picks up her bag and rushes down the street. She has just closed the door behind her when the storm arrives. Bang! Crash! Flash!

The storm carries on all through the night. But the next morning, the sun is shining again. What a beautiful day!

Making it Better

Poor Mummy is very sad. Someone, or something, has ruined the lovely plants in her garden.

'What has happened here?' she asks. Mason and Tasha hang their heads in shame. Their game of football has caused all of this mess.

Mummy makes them clean it all up. Then they have to go to the shops. As they pass the flower shop, Mason has an idea.

The children use their pocket money to buy a new plant for Mummy. She is very happy and surprised. They are good children, after all!

The New Arrival

Sammy Sloth is hanging around in the treetops. That's what sloths do. He is munching slowly on his favourite fruit.

Mummy Sloth crawls along to see him. 'I have some exciting news,' she says. 'You are going to have a baby brother!'

Sammy is not happy at all. He doesn't want to share his mummy with a new baby. He swims away in a sulk.

A few days later, Mummy has her baby. Sammy doesn't want to see it. But when he does, he falls in love. His baby brother is very, very cute!

The Big Race

Tammy and Ben have no school today. They are playing with their friends in the park.
'Let's have races!' shouts Nita, zooming along on her skates.

Michael and Alex rush off in front. Michael pedals very fast on his go-kart, but Alex overtakes him.

'We're coming!' shouts Ben. He and Tammy
try their hardest to catch up with the others.
Tammy wobbles and falls off. Ouch!

Daddy is worried about Tammy. It is a good job she was wearing her helmet. 'No more races, okay?' he says. 'Don't be silly, Daddy,' she says. 'I need to practise!'

The Little Hippo

Dandy is a little hippo in a big herd. She gets very frightened in a crowd. The adults are so big and noisy and heavy!

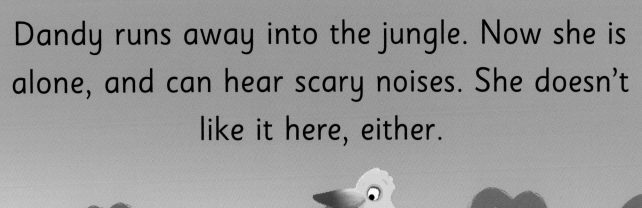

Dandy runs away into the jungle. Now she is alone, and can hear scary noises. She doesn't like it here, either.

The little hippo hears rushing water, and goes to explore. She sees two friends having fun. But it looks way too muddy for Dandy! Yuck.

'Why don't you take a swim?' asks her friend, Bird. 'That's what hippos are best at.' Sure enough, Dandy is very happy in the water.